## PARENTS: KEEP OUT!

Brian Moses lives in Sussex with his wife and two daughters. He travels the country performing his poems in schools and libraries. In his years as a parent he has learnt a lot from his daughters, including the art of staying calm whilst waiting for hours outside locked bathroom doors!

Lucy Maddison lives in Balham, South London with her partner Brian, daughter Sami and Jess the cat.

# PARENTS: KEEP OUT!

Poems chosen by Brian Moses
Illustrated by Lucy Maddison

MACMILLAN CHILDREN'S BOOKS

First published 2001
by Macmillan Children's Books
a division of Macmillan Publishers Ltd
This edition produced 2002 for The Book People Ltd
Hallwood Avenue, Haydock, St Helens
WA11 9UL

Associated companies throughout the world

ISBN 0 330 483471

3 5 7 9 8 6 4 2

A CIP catalogue record for this book is available from the British Library.

Printed by Mackays of Chatham plc, Chatham, Kent.

'Sorry' by Coral Rumble first published in *A Feast of Good Stories* by Lion.

# Contents

# This is a Contract

This is a contract
between (insert your name here)
and your mother/father/guardian/whatever
(who must be over the age of eighteen)
regarding access and entry to
the premises which hereinafter will be called
MY ROOM.

1. Never enter without knocking first
at least ten times
and loudly enough to be heard
over the *Titanic* theme tune.

2. Lower your eyes,
look at your feet:
this will ensure your safety
as the proprietor (me)
cannot guarantee
there will be no obstacles
(stray knickers, empty yoghurt tubs or my hamster)
in your way.

3. On entering MY ROOM
you must say **nothing, zero, zilch**
unless it is to pay me a compliment
about my school report
(and offer me a small reward)
or to tell me
there is a phone call from Leonardo Di Caprio
or that my real parents – the rich ones,
with the mansion in L.A. and the Cadillac –
have at last turned up to claim me back.

4. Should you break RULE THREE
there will be
the following levels of punishment:

Should you mention any of the following
  **BAD** words:
MESS/TIDY/DISGRACE/PIGSTY,
a curse will descend upon you
and the hair upon your head
will turn grey then fall out
in fist-sized clumps.

Should you say,
RIGHT YOUNG LADY,
your hearing will disappear
and from your nostrils will appear
spider-leg nasal hair.

Should you dare
to utter those cursed words,
THIS IS YOUR FINAL WARNING,
I will let my hamster run amok
in your underwear drawer
with instructions to chew
anything that is lacy, frilly, made of silk
or otherwise seems expensive.

Once signed the terms of this contract are legally binding.

**Parents please sign here**

.................................................

*Magi Gibson*

# My Mum
# Talks Too Much
## (to be spoken out loud in one breath)

The thing that I hate the most about
my mum is that she never stops
talking even when, or should I say
especially when, she has nothing
really important to say she just goes
on and on without ever taking a
breath or stopping to see if anyone
else wants to get a look-in on the
conversation which of course isn't
a real conversation at all if you get
my meaning because it's really just
a monologue a droning monotonous
monologue that you begin to feel will
never end at least not this side of the
next millennium and the worst thing of
all is that everybody else in our family
says that me and my mum are just as
bad as each other and that without any
shadow of a doubt at all or fear of
being contradicted we could both talk
the hindlegs off a whole herd of donkeys
and still find plenty more to talk about
and never once care about the fact that
nobody but nobody was paying any
attention to either of us at all.

*Mike Jubb*

# The School for Parents

At the school for parents
they have to work hard,
as they line up each morning
in the new parents' yard.

They all have lessons
on embarrassing their young,
and the best ways
of spoiling their fun.

They attend courses
on clothes with no style,
just in case they go out,
once in a while.

They're given talks
as they all work in pairs,
learning how to give
those fierce parent stares.

And when they're finished,
when they've passed the test,
when they're really
one of the best.

They're let out in the world
to be really bad,
just to drive us poor children
completely mad!

*Andrew Collett*

# My Mum Says...

My mum says
she never left dirty socks under the bed,
made mashed potato mountains with gravy rivers,
stuck chewing gum under the table,
broke a plate and hid the pieces.

My mum says
she always did her homework before tea,
cleaned the hamster cage without being told,
brushed her teeth before she went to bed,
kissed her aunts without pulling faces.

My gran says
my mum has a very short memory.

*Alison Chisholm*

# Fireworks

My mum and dad
are fireworks.
Light their fuses
and they're off,
exploding,
spitting furious sparks
in every direction.
And the trouble is,
these fireworks
are self-renewing.
Just when you think
they're all burnt out,
they start up
hissing and spluttering
all over again:
jumping-jacks
that never stop
jumping,
catherine wheels
that never stop
spinning,
volcanoes
that never stop
erupting.
Don't talk to me
about Guy Fawkes.
With parents like mine
who needs Firework Night?

*Penny Kent*

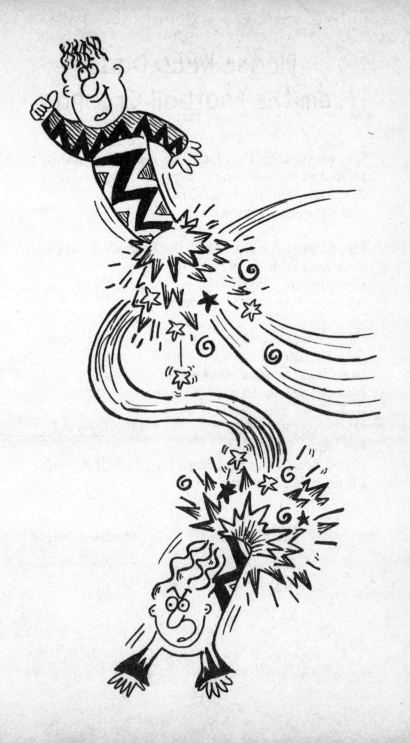

# Please Keep Dad
# from the Football Grounds

Oh, please keep Dad from the football grounds,
he makes me burn with shame
dancing round the boundaries
and roaring out my name.

Oh, please keep Dad from the football grounds,
he argues with the Ref
shouting his opinions.
It's enough to make you deaf.

Oh, please keep Dad from the football grounds,
he really shows me up,
swearing, chanting, singing.
It's not the F.A. Cup.

Oh, please keep Dad from the football grounds,
he's doing in my head.
If you don't keep Dad from the football grounds,
I'll do ballet instead!

*Marian Swinger*

# Super Trouble!

Do you know Superman and Superwoman?
Well I do because I've got them
as parents – **Superparents!**
(That's my mum and dad to you!)

You see my parents happen to have these
really annoying,
really irritating,
really unbearable,
and really unfair
**super powers!**

For example:

My dad has these X-ray eyes
that seem to know what I am thinking
before I actually think them.
Yesterday I heard, 'They'll be no sweets before tea.'
For goodness sake, he was in the next room
and I was only looking at the packet!

And he has this nose (it must be amplified!)
that can smell trouble anywhere, any place!
It's 'revenge time', you're creeping out
of your bedroom to dive-bomb your brother
when Dad's voice leaps largely up the stairs,
'And where do you think you're going, young man?'

Then there's Mum with her telescopic eyes,
scanning, searching for the slightest sign of dirt.
Her radar goes berserk after football – Beep! Beep!
**BEEP!!**
'Why are you covered in mud?'
'Well I was the goalkeeper, Mum.'
'Well next time stay away from the ball!'

And she's also got this amazing, extending neck
that allows her to be everywhere
and into everybody else's business.
In fact if it was long enough I'm sure
she would stick it up the chimney as a periscope
and scan the whole neighbourhood!

Superparents, super powers, **super trouble!**

*Ian Souter*

# With a Dad Like This, Who Needs Enemies!

A dad with shorts
As baggy and wrinkled as an elephant's skin,
Parading his pink and hairy knees all summer.
Who does Tom Jones impressions
In the middle of a crowded street
Just as I walk past him with my friends.

A dad who all of a sudden
Very loudly walks and talks like a Mad Robot
In the checkout queue at the supermarket,
And who makes mysterious whoopee cushion noises
Every time he runs upstairs.

A dad who jokes about the clothes I wear
And who hates all my music, who argues
With my teacher, the woman at the garage,
Shop assistants and the boy at the Burger Bar
Because French fries aren't proper chips.

A dad who pulls faces at me
When I'm on the school bus and who talks
In silly voices to all my friends, the kind of dad
Everyone else thinks is great
But nobody else has to live with him.
They don't know how tough that is!

*David Harmer*

# When I Grow Up
# and Have Children

When I grow up and have children,
And they ask if they can use the phone,
I'll tell them, 'You can't. If you want to call someone,
You'll have to buy a phone of your own.'

When I grow up and have children,
And they ask if they can stay up late,
I'll say, 'You can't. Even if you're eighteen,
You must be asleep by eight.'

When I grow up and have children,
And they ask if they can play in the street,
I'll say, 'No, you can't. What more do you want?
We've the backyard, that square of concrete.'

And when my children get angry and cry,
I'll ask them, 'What can I do?
I learnt everything I know from my mum.'
That's right, I'll blame it on you!

*Valerie Bloom*

# The Shouting Side

There's a war being waged
in our family,
Mum versus Dad,
in the middle there's me
and it's hard to decide
whose side I'm on
when they're both
on the shouting side.

Dad shouts at Mum,
Mum screams at Dad,
then they start on me
and it makes me mad.
I don't want to decide
whose side I'm on
when they're both
on the shouting side.

Can't they see,
can't they be quiet?
Why do they yell
like they're starting a riot?
They're acting this out
on a tiny stage,
there's no need to shout
or fly into a rage.

There's no need to take out
their feelings on me,
I'm trying to listen,
can't they see?
I'm standing here
with my ears wide open,
somebody please
be quietly spoken.

There's a war being waged
in our family,
Mum versus Dad,
in the middle there's me
and it's hard to decide
whose side I'm on
when they're both
on the shouting side.

*Brian Moses*

# You're Not Going Out Like That?

You're not going out?
Not looking like that?
You look just like something
Brought in by the cat.
People will laugh at you,
Neighbours will stare.
That outfit! Those colours!
And as for that hair . . .

You're not going out
When you look such a mess?
After all that I've said
About sensible dress!
I'll disown you! I promise!
I'm telling you flat:
You're not going out, Dad,
Not looking like that!

*Paul Bright*

# Telly

Sometimes, when I'm watching telly,
I say, 'What's happening?'
And they say, 'Shush!'
And I say, 'But what's happening?'
And they say, 'Be quiet!'
And I say, 'But I don't understand, what's happening?'
And they say, 'Neither do we,
Because *you* were talking!'

Sometimes, when I'm watching telly,
They'll come and switch it off,
And I say, 'I was watching that!'
And they say, 'What's it about?'
And I say, 'I don't know,
But it's good!'
And they say, 'Huh!'

Last night they were watching telly,
And I said, 'What's it about?'
And they said, 'Don't know.'
So I turned it off.

That's when I had to go to bed.

*Colin McEwan*

23

# What Time Do You Think This Is?

Well, on the dandelion clock
it's four puffs and a tiny wheeze.

On my wrist it's just as it always is –
a birthmark past a freckle.

According to the speaking clock
at the next pip it will be . . .

And my history teacher says
it's the start of the third millennium.

The moon says it's time for the owl to come out
and the tide says it's time for the sea to come in.

My broken watch says – well, what do you expect?
The same as always – ten to nine.

The clock on the cooker says it's time
to take the pizza out of the oven

and the clock in the car
says it's time to get going.

The DJ on the radio says
the night is yet young / it's time to hang loose.

My tummy clock says it's time for a feast.
My cool big cousin says – time doesn't exist!

The sundial says a cloud is passing by.
The water clock says time's dripping away

drip drop drip drop drip drop drip

and my mum says, 'What time do you think this is?
It's a simple enough question.'

And I'm just about to say
the dandelion clock says . . .

But I think it's time
to hold my tongue.


*Magi Gibson*

# Level Ten

I was going great guns.
I was doing fine.
I'd fought my way through level nine.
Then, just as I started level ten,
A shadow loomed behind my head.
It was Mum, saying, 'Bed!'
Just my luck!
My fingers slipped.
The aliens struck.

Although I've tried time and again,
I've never since reached level ten.

*John Foster*

# Doing Exactly
# as You're Told

*Do as you are told*, they say,
*Do exactly as you're told*,
*Do what I tell you*.

Parents . . . they think they're so clever
They think they know it all.

*Do
As
You
Are
Told!
Go and put your shoes and socks on.*

So I do.
Exactly as I'm told.

First my shoes
Then my socks,
Over the tops of my shoes so they stretch and go all
    wobbly at the front.

Mum comes in and goes ballistic . . .
*WHATDOYOUTHINKYOU'REDOING
    MUCKINGABOUTLIKETHAT?!*

I'm doing exactly as I'm told, Mum.
I'm putting my shoes ... and my socks on.

*DON'T BE SO STUPID! USE YOUR COMMON
SENSE!*

*Go and do your homework,* she said.
Where? I said.
*On the kitchen table,* she said.
So I did.
Exactly as I was told.
Forty-seven sums and a story about my dog.
On the kitchen table.
In fact I did so much
I had to go down one leg as well.

I'd just finished when Dad said,
*Do us a favour . . . turn the telly over.*
So I did.
Exactly as I was told.
I heaved and panted, pulled and pushed,
Grunted and groaned, nearly pulled a muscle,
Lifted and struggled until the screen was face down on
   the carpet.
*I can't see the football! What on earth are you doing!*

I'm doing exactly as I was told.
I'm turning the telly over.

Then I got shouted at and sent to bed.
Parents! They tell you off,
Even when you're doing
Exactly as you're told.


*Paul Cookson*

# At the Hairdresser's

This time I want something new.
Here's what I'd like you to do . . .
Short at the top, so I can spike it –
Use lots of gel.  Yes, I'm sure I'll like it.
Add blond streaks, they're really cool
And they'll impress my friends at school.
Shave in *Man U* at the back.
What do you mean, you'll get the sack?
What? Ask my mum?! OK, OK.
I'll have my usual cut today.


*Jane Clarke*

# Eat Your Greens, Miranda!

Eat your greens, Miranda,
Like a sensible young girl.
They'll put colour in your cheeks
And make your hair begin to curl.
They're good for your complexion,
They help you see at night.
Whatever's wrong, I tell you
Eating greens will put it right.
For an end to global warming,
Eat your greens – it just can't fail.
You can mend the ozone layer,
You can help to save the whale.
There'll be global peace and harmony
Before you reach your teens.
You can save the world, Miranda,
If you'll only eat your greens!

*Paul Bright*

# Recipe for an Argument

Take a slight difference of opinion
Between me and Dad.
Might be about homework,
Unsuitable viewing on TV,
Loud music,
Or just the way I am.
Add a hot temper with a sour voice. (Dad's.)
A dash of bitter intolerance. (Dad's.)
And a stubborn streak.
Well, two actually. His and mine.
Sprinkle liberally with tart comments. (Guess whose?)
Stir rapidly.
Bring to boil. (This is the easy part.)
Then turn down to a simmer
Until all ingredients melt in the mouth.
Serve warm with lashings of apologies. (Usually mine.
 This is the difficult part.)
Life is not fair in this house.
But I have to survive.

*Margaret Blount*

# Sorry

Why is the word 'sorry'
So very hard to say?
Your mouth goes dry,
Your arms go stiff,
Your knees start to give way.
And even when that little word
Is ready to pop out,
It rolls around
Upon your tongue
Until you have to shout,
'I'M SORRY!' just to get it past
Your gums, your teeth, your lips;
And then your mum says,
'Well, my girl,
It doesn't sound like it!'

*Coral Rumble*

# Turn it Down

'That deafening sound.
It makes my head go round and round.
I said, **TURN IT DOWN.**'

'But it has rhythm
It has heat,
It's hip, it's cool
Just tap your feet.
Come on, Dad, just let yourself go,
You'll get to like it.
It'll grow on you.'

'That deafening sound.
It makes my head go round and round.
Turn it down.
I said, **TURN IT DOWN**.'

'Feel the vibration
In the beat.
Relax. Enjoy it.
It's really neat.
Come on, Dad, I'll bet you can move.
Give it a try.
Come on, let's groove.'

'That deafening sound.
It makes my head go round and round
TURN IT DOWN!
I said, **TURN IT DOWN**.'

'Dad, do you remember what Grandad said about the
Beatles?'

*Margaret Blount*

# Percy

I keep a secret in my room,
A pig called Percy.
He lives in a sty under the bed.
He's no trouble.
A bit noisy – Percy likes to dance a jig –
But he'll eat anything,
Old socks,
Orange peel,
School reports,
Dentist's appointments,
Greens.
He's especially handy when Mum's spring-cleaning,
Rooting around or being a busybody.
Although, last week I had a shock.
She called to me from the kitchen,
'Have you cleaned out that pigsty yet?'
She's no fool, my mother,
She might have heard Percy dancing.
So I've taught him the soft-shoe-shuffle.
As a precaution.

*Mary Green*

# Empty
# Space

There's a hole in our house
But you can't see it.
There's a hole in our house
But the rain can't come through.
There's a hole in our house
But sneaky mice
Winds like ice
Cracks in walls
Gaping doors
Aren't the problem.

There's a hole in our house
And nothing can fill it.
There's a hole in our house
Since Dad left.

*Patricia Leighton*

# If You Were Me

If you were me
and I were you,
I'd let *you* buy
those platform shoes;
I'd understand that
when you're young
the most important
words are FUN
and NOW
and YES and FREE,
if I were you
and you were me.

If I were you
and you were me,
I'd say, 'OK
then, climb that tree:
don't even stop
when at the top;
keep reaching for
the moon and sun.
Do what you
*have* to do,'
if you were me
and I were you.

*Mike Johnson*

# Dear Parents Everywhere

We know how much you hate JUNK MAIL. We all do.
HONESTLY. But this letter is DIFFERENT.
It could CHANGE YOUR LIVES. For the BETTER.
And for GOOD. So don't throw it away. PLEASE.
SIMPLY READ the next paragraph.

Just learn the following phrases OFF BY HEART and
use them AS OFTEN AS YOU CAN when you are
with your CHILDREN and in NO TIME AT ALL
your QUALITY OF LIFE will GREATLY IMPROVE.
Please send NO MONEY – just do as we say – simply
LEARN and USE THESE PHRASES!!!

Why don't you watch TV all day long?

Hey, turn the music up REALLY LOUD, it's great!

What time would you like to go to bed?

Go outside? What for? Play your new computer game!

No, honestly. Stay in bed. I'll feed the rabbits.

Don't bother tidying your room, it'll be in a mess again in minutes!

I do care who started it. They'll be punished, don't you worry.

So how much pocket money would you like in future?

Please let us know how you got on:

I used those phrases and now –

a. we're all happy all the time
b. the kids are happy all the time
c. you're right, it's changed our lives completely
d. we're broke

email your response to www.kidzeverywhere.com

*James Carter*

# Home Time

My dad's in the playground
To meet me from school.
'Hello there! How are you?'
(He smiles like a fool.)

'That's simply terrific.
You've just made my day.'
(He's talking too loudly.
I groan. Look away.)

'And how was your morning?
Your long afternoon?'
(I kick a small pebble,
I hum a sad tune.)

My dad's really friendly,
So why should I moan?
(He'll speak to me soon –
When he's switched off his phone.)

*Clare Bevan*

# Moment

In a moment
I'll do my homework
in a moment
I'll take the look off my face
in a moment
in just a moment
when this programme finishes
in a moment
when I've found a pencil
in a moment
when you stop nagging me
in a moment
in just a moment
when pigs float past the window
any moment
now
what's that?
my friends are at the door
and want to play out?
I'm there already.

*Dave Calder*

# Now Look What You've Made Me Do!

'There's no point *playing* football.
You must put the boot in,' Dad says.
I kick and miss the bull's-eyed wall.
'No! Not like that!'
He whops the ball!
Thrash! Wallop! Chop! The tulip heads!
'Now look what you've made me do!' he says.

'There's no point *trying* woodwork.
Hit the nail on the head,' Dad says.
I rap my thumb. He goes berserk.
'Quick strike! Like this!'
My handiwork!
Split! Crack! Smash! Ouch! My rabbit hutch!
'Now look what you've made me do!' he says.

'There's no point *plucking* that thing.
You must strike a chord,' Dad says.
I strum in C and start to sing.
'Too soft! Full bass!'
It's deafening!
Zing! Twang! Bong! Ping! He's snapped each string!
'Now look what you've made me do!' he says.

*Mina Johnson*

# How Can I?

How can I wind up my brother
when I haven't got the key?

How can I turn on my charm
when I can't even find the switch?

How can I snap at my mother
when I'm not a crocodile?

How can I stir up my sister
when I'm not even holding a spoon?

How can I pick up my feet
and not fall to the ground on my knees?

How can I stretch my legs
when they're long enough already?

Parents! They ask the impossible!

*Brian Moses*

# Flying the Kite

'Let's go out and fly your kite,'
Dad says to me. I say, 'Alright,'
and off we go to One Tree Hill.
Although the air is calm and still
out the kite comes and I try
to get it up into the sky.
The kite just flops and drags along
the ground. Dad says,
'You've done that wrong.'
It's then the wind begins to blow.
'I'll try,' says Dad. 'There, up she goes.'
'Let me have a go,' I shout.
Dad just lets more kite string out . . .
It swoops, stampedes a herd of cows.
'Dad,' I howl, 'it's my turn now.'
'Not yet,' says Dad. 'I'll just try this.'
The kite bombs past us with a hiss
then rockets upwards into space.
I see the smug look on Dad's face.
I grab the string, the kite breaks free
and ends up tangled in a tree.
Dad yells, I sulk and we don't speak
to one another for a week.

*Marian Swinger*

# How to Ask for a Hamster
## (for Tamara)

Mum, can I keep a snake in my room?
*What did you say? Are you mad?*
Well, Jamie keeps a snake in *his* room,
He got it from his dad.

Will you buy me a mongoose, Mum?
I've played with one; it belongs to Maria,
It's really docile, can I, please, Mum?
*I don't think that's a good idea!*

Can I have a pony then?
I could afford to pay for hay.
*D'you know how much a pony costs?*
Japhet got one for *his* birthday.

How about a crocodile?
They sell them in Didcot.
I think that's where Chloe bought hers.
Can I have one? *Certainly NOT!*

I'll settle for a tarantula then,
It would be in a cage, of course.
Joshua has a tarantula.
*Oh no! I can think of nothing worse!*

What about a little monkey?
Tina has a chimpanzee.
Everyone in class has a pet,
Everybody except me.

You can have a cat, or a hamster,
You cannot have a snake or mouse.
No crocs, monkey or creepy-crawlies
I won't have a zoo in this house.

OK, I'll settle for a hamster,
It's better than nothing, I suppose.
Oh, there's the doorbell, must be Jamie,
We promised to go and play at Joe's.

Jamie, you were right, I tried it,
Just like you said, it worked a treat,
I'm getting the hamster, now tell me,
How do I ask for a parakeet?

*Valerie Bloom*

# MY GANG

Poems about friendship chosen by Brian Moses

## Gangs

They were just boys together
with no girls allowed.
They acted all tough
and went out in a crowd.
They wore scruffy jeans
on their trips to the park
where they trundled
a football around until dark.
And, chattering and giggling
(an ear-splitting noise),
the girls on the swings
would make fun of the boys.
But, as the boys scornfully
sauntered away,
they knew in their hearts
girls would get them some day.

*Marian Swinger*

# A selected list of poetry books available from Macmillan Children's Books

The prices shown below are correct at the time of going to press. However, Macmillan Publishers reserve the right to show new retail prices on covers which may differ from those previously advertised.

---

**The Secret Lives of Teachers**
Revealing rhymes, chosen by Brian Moses
0 330 34265 7
£3.50

**Aliens Stole My Underpants**
And other intergalactic poems, chosen by Brian Moses
0 330 34995 3
£2.99

**Parent-Free Zone**
Poems about parents, chosen by Brian Moses
0 330 34554 0
£2.99

**Don't Look at Me in That Tone of Voice**
Poems by Brian Moses
0 330 35337 3
£2.99

**Never Play Snap with a Shark**
Poems chosen by John Foster
0 330 39370 7
£3.99

**Welcome to the Snake Hotel**
Slithering poems chosen by Brian Moses
0 330 48261 0
£3.50

**The Penguin in the Fridge**
And other cool poems by Peter Dixon
0 330 48019 7
£3.50

---

All Macmillan titles can be ordered at your local bookshop or are available by post from:

**Book Service by Post**
**PO Box 29, Douglas, Isle of Man IM99 1BQ**

Credit cards accepted. For details:
Telephone: 01624 675137
Fax: 01624 670923
E-mail: bookshop@enterprise.net

**Free postage and packing in the UK.**
Overseas customers: add £1 per book (paperback)
and £3 per book (hardback).